Jess and Joe Go to the Dentist

written by Jay Dale

illustrated by Katriona Chapman

Jess and Joe
went to the dentist.

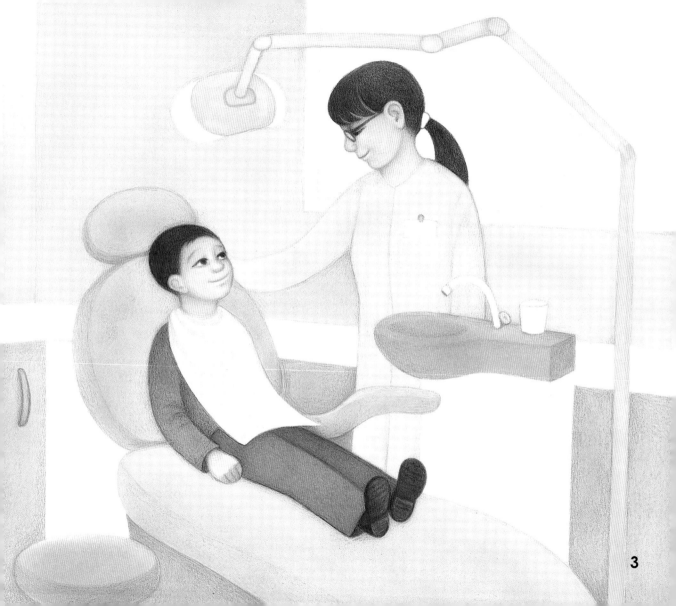

"I have all of my teeth,"
said Jess.
"Will one of my teeth
come out?"

"Yes," said the dentist.
"One of your teeth
will come out."

6

"I have all of my teeth, too,"
said Joe.
"Will one of my teeth come out?"

"Yes," said the dentist.
"One of your teeth
will come out, too."

Jess and Joe
went home with Dad.

Jess looked in the mirror.
She went up and down
with one little tooth.

Joe looked in the mirror, too.
He went up and down
with one little tooth.

Joe's tooth went up and down.

Jess's tooth went up and down, too.

"Yes!" said Jess.
"My tooth came out!"

"Yes!" said Joe.
"My tooth came out, too!"

"Look!" said Jess.

"I have one little tooth."

"Yes!" said Joe.

"I have one little tooth, too!"